JASON
QUEST FOR THE GOLDEN FLEECE

A
GREEK
MYTH

STORY BY
JEFF LIMKE

PENCILS BY
TIM SEELEY

INKS BY
BARBARA SCHULZ

BASED ON
THE HEROIC POEM
BY APOLLONIUS
OF RHODES

EUROPE

ITALY

N

MEDITERRANEAN SEA

JASON
QUEST FOR THE GOLDEN FLEECE

COLCHIS

BLACK SEA

BITHYNIA

A
GREEK
MYTH

GREECE

HELLESPONT

AEGEAN SEA

THESSALY

IOLCUS

ATHENS

GRAPHIC UNIVERSE™

THE LEGEND OF JASON AND THE OTHER GREEK HEROES ABOARD THE *ARGO* AND THEIR QUEST FOR THE GOLDEN FLEECE MAY HAVE ORIGINATED AS A STORY TOLD ABOUT THE FIRST GREAT SAILING SHIPS BUILT BY THE ANCIENT GREEKS. THE LEGEND AS IT IS TOLD TODAY WAS FIRST WRITTEN IN ABOUT 280 BC BY APOLLONIUS OF RHODES, A LIBRARIAN AT THE GREAT LIBRARY IN ALEXANDRIA, EGYPT. THE AUTHOR ALSO BASED THIS VERSION ON THE RETELLINGS IN *BULFINCH'S MYTHOLOGY*, *MYTHOLOGY* BY EDITH HAMILTON AND *THE FRIENDLY GUIDE TO MYTHOLOGY* BY NANCY HATHAWAY. DAVID MULROY OF THE UNIVERSITY OF WISCONSIN-MILWAUKEE ENSURED HISTORICAL AND VISUAL ACCURACY.

STORY BY JEFF LIMKE

PENCILS BY TIM SEELEY

INKS BY BARBARA SCHULZ

COLOURING BY HI-FI DESIGN

LETTERING BY RAY DILLON

CONSULTANT: DAVID MULROY, UNIVERSITY OF WISCONSIN-MILWAUKEE

This book was first published in the USA in 2007. First published in the UK in 2008 by Lerner Books, Dalton House, 60 Windsor Avenue, London, SW19 2RR

Website address: www.lernerbooks.co.uk

This edition was updated and edited for UK publication by Discovery Books Ltd., Unit 3, 37 Watling Street, Leintwardine, Shropshire, SY7 0LW

British Library Cataloguing in Publication Data

Limke, Jeff
    Jason : quest for the golden fleece. - (Graphic myths and legends series)
    1. Jason (Greek mythology) - Comic books, strips, etc. - Juvenile fiction 2. Children's stories - Comic books, strips, etc.
    I. Title II. Seely, Tim
    741.5

ISBN-13: 978 1 58013 321 0

Printed in China

TABLE OF CONTENTS

THE CLASHING ROCKS

MY NAME IS JASON, AND I SHOULD BE THE RULER OF IOLCUS.

MY FATHER, AESON, HAD THE THRONE TAKEN AWAY FROM HIM BY HIS BROTHER PELIAS. MY FATHER HID ME FROM THE EVIL PELIAS, AND I WAS RAISED BY A CENTAUR, HALF MAN, HALF HORSE, NAMED CHIRON. CHIRON TAUGHT ME WELL WHO I WAS AND WHAT I WAS SUPPOSED TO BE.

WHEN I ARRIVED IN IOLCUS TO CLAIM MY BIRTHRIGHT, MY UNCLE DIDN'T GIVE THE THRONE TO ME. HE SAID HE WOULD ACCEPT MY CLAIM TO THE THRONE ONLY IF I BROUGHT HIM THE FLEECE OF THE GOLDEN RAM OF COLCHIS.

HE SAID BRINGING THE GOLDEN FLEECE TO IOLCUS WOULD GRANT HIM PEACE FROM THE GHOST OF PHRIXUS, WHO HAUNTED HIM NIGHTLY. AND THE ADVENTURE WOULD BRING TO ME GREAT GLORY.

I BUILT A GREAT SHIP AND NAMED IT THE ARGO, AND I GATHERED ALL THE HEROES I COULD FIND TO JOIN ME ON IT.

WE ARGONAUTS TRAVELLED FAR ON OUR SEARCH AND HAD MANY ADVENTURES.

THE HEROES INCLUDED NOBLE AND VIRTUOUS PELEUS WHO WAS GIVEN A SEA GODDESS TO WED, AND ZETES AND CALAIS THE SONS OF BOREAS, THE NORTH WIND.

BLIND PHINEUS, WHOM THE HEROES SAVED FROM STARVATION, RODE WITH US AS WELL.

OTHERS, SUCH AS HERCULES, HAD LEFT US EARLIER.

HERCULES HAD SAVED HIS ARMOUR-BEARER HYLAS FROM DROWNING AND HAD STAYED BEHIND TO MAKE SURE HE RETURNED TO GOOD HEALTH.

THE TWINS, CASTOR AND POLLUX, BROUGHT THEIR YOUTHFUL ENERGY, WHILE ORPHEUS BROUGHT HIS LYRE TO KEEP US ENTERTAINED.

THEN A NEW DANGER PUT OUR VERY LIVES AT RISK.

JASON, I CAN TELL FROM THE SOUNDS THAT WE ARE NEAR THE ROCKS KNOWN AS THE SYMPLEGADES. I TOLD YOU ABOUT THEM. NO SHIP HAS EVER PASSED THROUGH THEM SAFELY.

YOU'RE SURE, PHINEUS? THEY LOOK RATHER ORDINARY TO ME.

ORDINARY? THOSE ROCKS WILL CRASH TOGETHER AND CRUSH WHATEVER TRIES TO GO BETWEEN THEM.

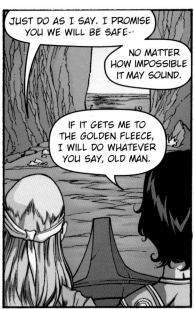

JUST DO AS I SAY. I PROMISE YOU WE WILL BE SAFE--

NO MATTER HOW IMPOSSIBLE IT MAY SOUND.

IF IT GETS ME TO THE GOLDEN FLEECE, I WILL DO WHATEVER YOU SAY, OLD MAN.

THE MEN MUST ROW AS HARD AS THEY CAN. WE MUST BE MOVING AS FAST AS POSSIBLE.

WHEN WE ARE ALMOST TO THE ROCKS, I WILL RELEASE THIS DOVE, AND IT WILL FLY AHEAD OF US.

THE ROCKS WILL CLOSE UPON THE DOVE. PERHAPS THEY WILL CRUSH IT, PERHAPS NOT.

THE ROCKS WILL THEN PULL BACK, AND AS THEY DO SO, WE CAN SAIL SWIFTLY BETWEEN THEM BEFORE THEY CAN CRASH TOGETHER AGAIN.

YOU ARE RIGHT. IT DOES SOUND IMPOSSIBLE.

TO ME, THOSE ROCKS DON'T LOOK AS IF THEY WILL EVER MOVE, BUT I HAVE BEEN WRONG BEFORE. WE WILL DO WHAT YOU SAY.

ROW! ROW AS IF YOUR LIFE DEPENDS ON IT--

BECAUSE IT DOES!

IN THE NAME OF ZEUS, RULER OF THE GODS!

ROW!

ROW! IF YOU ARE THE HEROES YOU CLAIM TO BE, ROW!

ROW! ROW! ROW!

MY THANKS, ZEUS.

WE MADE IT THROUGH ALIVE.

AND THANKS TO THE GODDESS ATHENA. YOU TOLD ME SHE GAVE YOU PART OF THIS SHIP.

MY THANKS TO YOU, PHINEUS, TOO. I DIDN'T BELIEVE THAT THE ROCKS WERE DANGEROUS, BUT THE GODS TOLD YOU TRUE WHAT TO DO.

YOU SAVED ME FROM STARVATION. IT IS ONLY RIGHT I HELP YOU ON YOUR QUEST.

HEROES, YOU HAVE ROWED HARD AND YOU HAVE MY THANKS. THIS PUTS US CLOSER TO THE FLEECE.

I NOW ASK ORPHEUS, MASTER MUSICIAN, TO REWARD YOU WITH SONGS OF PAST DEEDS AND OF WHAT YOU DID TODAY.

ORPHEUS PLAYED HIS LYRE ON INTO THE NIGHT. HIS TALES OF WONDER AND HEROISM, ENHANCED BY HIS MELODIOUS VOICE, CAPTIVATED US ALL.

THE GODS HAD SUPPORTED US THUS FAR. I BELIEVED THEY WOULD CONTINUE TO DO SO AS LONG AS WE REMEMBERED TO HONOUR THEM.

IN HONOUR OF ZEUS, GOD OF THE SKY AND THUNDERBOLTS; HERA, HIS WIFE AND GODDESS OF THE HOME; AND POSEIDON, GOD OF THE WATERS WE SAILED UPON—

I GIVE THIS PART OF OUR CELEBRATION IN THANKS AND INVITE THEM TO JOIN US—

—AND ASK THEM TO TAKE US QUICKLY TO COLCHIS, HOME OF THE GOLDEN FLEECE.

11

LAND!

IT'S COLCHIS!

YOU COME FROM IOLCUS? WHAT BRINGS YOU HERE FROM SO FAR AWAY?

I MUST SPEAK WITH YOUR KING. HE HAS SOMETHING I NEED.

THE PALACE IS TOO FAR TO REACH TONIGHT. YOU CAN CAMP ALONG THE SHORE AND START OUT IN THE MORNING.

BUT BE CAREFUL. KING AEETES IS A POWERFUL MAN WITH A POWERFUL FAMILY.

THAT'S FINE. WE ARE STRONG TOO.

SET UP CAMP HERE. WE'LL GO TO THE PALACE AT SUNRISE.

THE ORIGIN OF THE GOLDEN FLEECE

JASON, TELL US THE STORY OF HOW THE GOLDEN FLEECE CAME TO COLCHIS.

I AM FLATTERED THAT YOU CHOOSE ME TO TELL IT RATHER THAN ORPHEUS, BUT VERY WELL, PELEUS, I SHALL DO MY BEST.

KING ATHAMAS OF IOLCUS HAD TIRED OF HIS OLD WIFE, QUEEN NEPHELE, AND HAD TAKEN INO, A YOUNGER WOMAN, TO BE HIS QUEEN.

NEPHELE FEARED FOR HER CHILDREN. SHE WORRIED THAT THE NEW QUEEN WOULD TRY TO KILL THEM. THEN THE CHILDREN OF INO WOULD BE IN LINE TO BECOME THE NEXT RULERS.

AND INO DID SCHEME.

SHE HEATED THE CITY'S SEED SUPPLY SO THAT THE SEED GRAIN WOULDN'T SPROUT. THERE WAS NO GRAIN AT THE NEXT HARVEST, AND THE PEOPLE WERE STARVING.

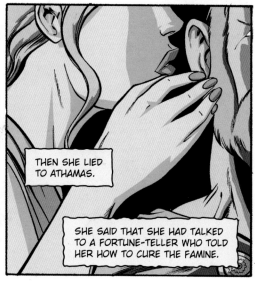

THEN SHE LIED TO ATHAMAS.

SHE SAID THAT SHE HAD TALKED TO A FORTUNE-TELLER WHO TOLD HER HOW TO CURE THE FAMINE.

SHE TOLD HIM HE WOULD HAVE TO SACRIFICE HIS CHILDREN BY NEPHELE TO ZEUS AND HERA.

NEPHELE PRAYED TO THE GODS TO PROTECT HER AND HER CHILDREN.

IT LOOKED AS THOUGH THE GODS HAD IGNORED HER.

NEPHELE TRIED TO SAVE HER CHILDREN. SHE BEGGED FOR THEIR LIVES AS THE GUARDS RESTRAINED HER.

THE BOY, PHRIXUS, AND THE GIRL, HELLE, GIGGLED AS THEY LOOKED UP AT THEIR FATHER. THEY THOUGHT HE WAS PLAYING SOME SORT OF GAME.

THEY WERE WRONG. DISTRAUGHT, NEPHELE CALLED OUT ONCE MORE TO THE GODS TO SAVE HER CHILDREN.

THE GODS HAD HEARD HER.

ZEUS SENT A GOLDEN RAM TO SAVE THE CHILDREN.

THE RAM FLEW OFF TOWARD A PLACE WHERE THE CHILDREN WOULD BE SAFE.

HELLE BECAME SO EXCITED, SHE LOST HER GRIP AND FELL INTO THE SEA BELOW. THE GODS CALLED THE PLACE WHERE SHE LANDED THE HELLESPONT IN HER HONOUR.

THE RAM FINALLY LANDED HERE IN COLCHIS.

KING AEETES AND PHRIXUS SHEARED THE RAM OF ITS GOLDEN FLEECE BEFORE PHRIXUS OFFERED THE ANIMAL TO ZEUS IN THANKS FOR HIS SAFE ARRIVAL.

PHRIXUS THEN MARRIED AEETES' SISTER CHALCIOPE, AND THEY HAD FIVE CHILDREN TOGETHER.

WHEN I RETURN WITH THE FLEECE, PELIAS WILL HAVE NO CHOICE BUT TO ACCEPT MY RIGHT TO RULE IOLCUS.

15

THE KING OF COLCHIS

DURING THE NIGHT, HERA CAME TO ME IN A DREAM. SHE SAID SHE WOULD HELP ME TO GET INSIDE THE PALACE SAFELY. I WAS TO TAKE WITH ME PHRONTIS AND MECAS, THE SONS OF PHRIXUS AND CHALCIOPE, WHOM WE HAD RESCUED; TWO OF MY CHOSEN HEROES; CASTOR AND POLLUS; NOBLE PELEUS, AND THE STORYTELLER ORPHEUS.

THAT MORNING ALL I COULD THINK OF WAS MEETING WITH THE KING, TAKING THE FLEECE, AND RETURNING HOME.

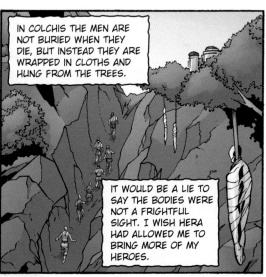

IN COLCHIS THE MEN ARE NOT BURIED WHEN THEY DIE, BUT INSTEAD THEY ARE WRAPPED IN CLOTHS AND HUNG FROM THE TREES.

IT WOULD BE A LIE TO SAY THE BODIES WERE NOT A FRIGHTFUL SIGHT. I WISH HERA HAD ALLOWED ME TO BRING MORE OF MY HEROES.

PRAISE HERA, WE ARE HERE.

YOUR MOTHER LIVES IN A VERY NICE PLACE. ONLY THE GODS COULD HAVE PROVIDED SUCH MAGNIFICENT THINGS, PHRONTIS.

YES, HEPHAESTUS, THE GODS' BLACKSMITH, GAVE THEM TO OUR GREAT-GRANDFATHER.

HALT! WHO GOES THERE?

DON'T MOVE!

KEEP YOUR HANDS WHERE WE CAN SEE THEM!

PHRONTIS?

MOTHER!

MELAS!

I HAVE MISSED YOU BOTH SO MUCH!

WHERE HAVE YOU BEEN FOR SO LONG?

IT IS A LONG AND SAD STORY.

I—I DON'T THINK I CAN TELL IT. MAYBE SOMEONE ELSE CAN.

IF YOU WANT ME TO, CHALCIOPE, I CAN TELL THE TALE OF YOUR CHILDREN.

YES, I WOULD LIKE THAT VERY MUCH.

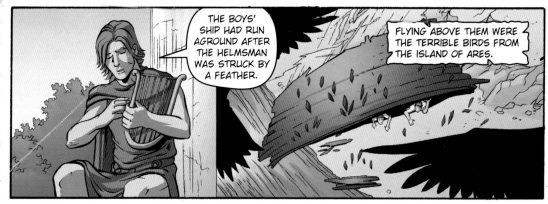

THE BOYS' SHIP HAD RUN AGROUND AFTER THE HELMSMAN WAS STRUCK BY A FEATHER.

FLYING ABOVE THEM WERE THE TERRIBLE BIRDS FROM THE ISLAND OF ARES.

THE BIRDS DEFEND THEMSELVES BY LOOSENING FEATHERS FROM THEIR BODIES AND LETTING THEM DROP.

THE POINT OF THE QUILL IS AS SHARP AS A SPEAR AND JUST AS DEADLY.

MELAS! *THERE! DO YOU SEE IT?*

IT'S AN ILLUSION OFF THE WATER, PHRONTIS.

NO, LOOK CLOSER—

MELAS! THEY SEE IT TOO!

HERE! HERE!

LOOK HERE!

A FIRE! WE NEED A FIRE!

PRAY TO HERA AND ZEUS THAT THEY SEE IT.

PRAY TO POSEIDON TO LET THEM COME THIS WAY.

–JASON OF IOLCUS, A MAN WHO WOULD BE KING. MY MEN HAVE TOLD ME OF YOUR SHIP DOCKED BELOW. I HAD THOUGHT PELIAS RULED IOLCUS.

TELL ME WHAT I SEEM TO BE MISSING.

NOT ONLY AN UPSTART BUT RUDE AS WELL.

SPEAK TO ME, BEFORE I HAVE YOU EXECUTED FOR ANNOYING ME.

NO, FATHER, PLEASE.

I-I-I'M SORRY, KING.

YOU ARE LUCKY, JASON. MY DAUGHTER, MEDEA HAS CALMED MY ANGER ... FOR THE MOMENT.

IN ORDER TO CLAIM MY BIRTHRIGHT AND SOOTHE THE RESTLESS SPIRIT OF PHRIXUS, I ASK OF YOU—

—THE GOLDEN FLEECE.

WHAT!

TEST HIM, FATHER. MAKE HIM PROVE HE IS WHO HE SAYS HE IS.

A GOOD IDEA.

GUARD!

I WILL DO WHATEVER IS ASKED.

THE GODS ARE WITH ME AND BLESS MY QUEST.

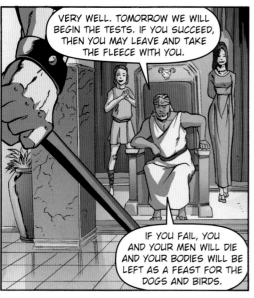

VERY WELL. TOMORROW WE WILL BEGIN THE TESTS. IF YOU SUCCEED, THEN YOU MAY LEAVE AND TAKE THE FLEECE WITH YOU.

IF YOU FAIL, YOU AND YOUR MEN WILL DIE AND YOUR BODIES WILL BE LEFT AS A FEAST FOR THE DOGS AND BIRDS.

BUT OF COURSE. I WOULD HAVE IT NO OTHER WAY.

WE HAVE BEEN TALKING AMONG US WHILE YOU ATE.

ARE YOU WILLING TO DO THIS, PERHAPS SACRIFICE EVERYONE HERE, TO GET THE FLEECE? YOU KNOW ANY OF US WOULD BE WILLING TO DO IT FOR YOU.

CASTOR, I HELPED MAKE SURE YOUR BROTHER POLLUX WASN'T PURSUED WHEN HE DEFEATED THE KING OF BITHYNIA, DIDN'T I?

YES, BUT—

BUT NOTHING. I SUCCEEDED THEN. I WILL NOW. PERHAPS YOU SHOULD LET YOUR BROTHER AND THE OTHERS SPEAK FOR THEMSELVES.

IF YOU WANT TO LEAVE, GO NOW AND DON'T LOOK BACK. YOU KNEW WHAT YOU SIGNED ON FOR WHEN WE LEFT.

DON'T CALL ME A COWARD! I WOULDN'T BE HERE IF I FELT THIS WAS A DOOMED QUEST!

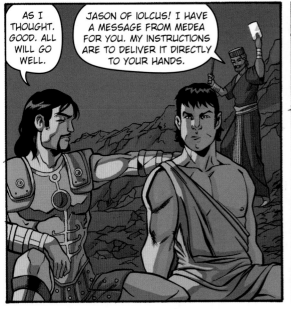

AS I THOUGHT. GOOD. ALL WILL GO WELL.

JASON OF IOLCUS! I HAVE A MESSAGE FROM MEDEA FOR YOU. MY INSTRUCTIONS ARE TO DELIVER IT DIRECTLY TO YOUR HANDS.

MEDEA? FOR ME? WHY?

SHE IS THE KING'S DAUGHTER. IT IS NOT MY PLACE TO QUESTION HER.

23

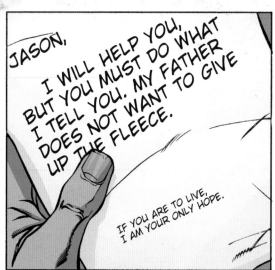

JASON,
I WILL HELP YOU, BUT YOU MUST DO WHAT I TELL YOU. MY FATHER DOES NOT WANT TO GIVE UP THE FLEECE.

IF YOU ARE TO LIVE, I AM YOUR ONLY HOPE.

...OU. ...NOT WANT ...E FLEECE.

IF YOU ARE TO LIVE, I AM YOUR ONLY HOPE.

I'M NOT SURE I UNDERSTAND. HOW CAN SHE HELP ME?

SHE'S A WITCH, AND A GOOD ONE. SHE KEEPS IT SECRET FROM HER FATHER SO HE DOES NOT SEE HER AS A THREAT TO HIS THRONE.

TOMORROW AT SUNRISE, YOU ARE TO MEET HER HERE, BY THE GATE. SHE WILL HAVE WHAT YOU NEED TO SUCCEED.

THANK YOU. BUT WHY IS SHE HELPING ME?

SHE MUST LIKE YOU.

YOU ARE BEAUTIFUL. BUT WHY ARE YOU HELPING ME?

YOU'RE THE FIRST PRINCE TO EVER COME FOR THE FLEECE. MY BROTHER THINKS YOU ARE THE GREATEST HERO HE'S EVER SEEN.

HE THINKS YOU'RE SPECIAL.

SO DO I.

ARE YOU CRAZY? YOU'RE WILLING TO BETRAY YOUR FATHER FOR ME?

WHEN EROS'S ARROWS STRIKE A PERSON, THEY ARE SMITTEN. EVERYONE KNOWS THAT. WHO ARE WE TO DENY THE GODS?

I FELT EROS'S STING TOO. BUT HELPING ME IS DANGEROUS FOR BOTH OF US. YOUR FATHER WILL FEEL BETRAYED.

NOT TO MAKE SURE THAT YOU STAY ALIVE, MY LOVE, WOULD BE A BETRAYAL OF MY HEART, AND THAT WOULD BE WORSE.

WHEN I GET THE FLEECE, THEN PERHAPS I CAN TALK TO YOUR FATHER ABOUT TAKING YOU TO IOLCUS.

YES?

EROS DID STRIKE BOTH OF US AND ...

... I COULD ASK YOUR FATHER FOR YOUR HAND AND THEN ...

AND?

YES!!

I MUST GET BACK BEFORE I AM MISSED, BUT WHEN YOU THINK YOU HAVE LOST, REMEMBER HOW CADMUS, THE FOUNDER OF THEBES, THREW THE STONES TO DEFEAT THE DEAD SOLDIERS.

AND PROMISE NEVER TO FORGET ME OR WHAT YOU SAID.

NEVER!

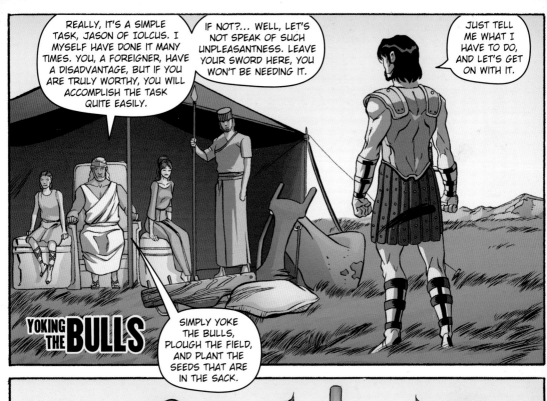

YOKING THE BULLS

... I WOULDN'T HAVE STOOD A CHANCE WITHOUT THE POLE.

WITH GOATS, I COULD BE MY OWN ANCHOR, BUT WITH A BULL THIS SIZE ...

YAH! BULL!

IT WORKED—JUST AS IT DID BACK WHEN I WAS WITH CHIRON.

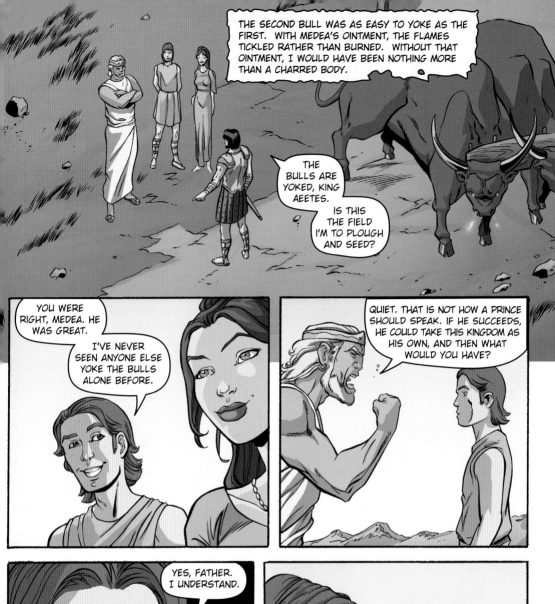

THE SECOND BULL WAS AS EASY TO YOKE AS THE FIRST. WITH MEDEA'S OINTMENT, THE FLAMES TICKLED RATHER THAN BURNED. WITHOUT THAT OINTMENT, I WOULD HAVE BEEN NOTHING MORE THAN A CHARRED BODY.

THE BULLS ARE YOKED, KING AEETES.

IS THIS THE FIELD I'M TO PLOUGH AND SEED?

YOU WERE RIGHT, MEDEA. HE WAS GREAT.

I'VE NEVER SEEN ANYONE ELSE YOKE THE BULLS ALONE BEFORE.

QUIET. THAT IS NOT HOW A PRINCE SHOULD SPEAK. IF HE SUCCEEDS, HE COULD TAKE THIS KINGDOM AS HIS OWN, AND THEN WHAT WOULD YOU HAVE?

YES, FATHER. I UNDERSTAND.

HAVING PLOUGHED AND SEEDED BEFORE, I KNEW WHAT TO EXPECT, NOT LIKE YOKING THOSE BULLS.

THAT HAD SCARED ME, BUT WITH MEDEA'S OINTMENT, IT WENT WELL.

SOWING THE FIELDS

ALL I HAD TO DO WAS TAKE A HANDFUL OF SEEDS AND SPRINKLE THEM INTO THE FURROW LEFT BY THE PLOUGH.

THIS WAS TOO EASY.

THE SEEDS WERE BIG. BIGGER THAN ANY I KNEW ABOUT.

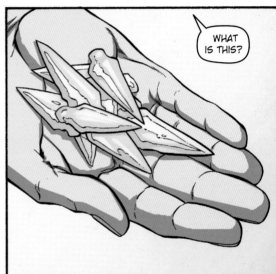

WHAT IS THIS?

WHAT KIND OF SEEDS *ARE* THESE?

WHAT ARE THESE? WHAT DO THEY GROW?

THEY ARE DRAGON'S TEETH. BUT YOU'LL HAVE TO WAIT AND SEE WHAT WE HARVEST.

DRAGON'S TEETH? WHAT IS THIS ABOUT?

WHAT IS KING AEETES TRYING TO DO?

WHAT IS THE TRICK HERE?

I KNOW HE'S TRYING TO FOOL ME.

WERE THE BULLS THE EASY PART? THE DIVERSION?

WHAT AM I MISSING?

THAT'S IT!
CADMUS'S STRATEGY!

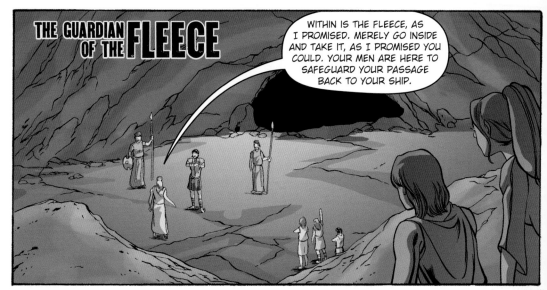

THE GUARDIAN OF THE FLEECE

WITHIN IS THE FLEECE, AS I PROMISED. MERELY GO INSIDE AND TAKE IT, AS I PROMISED YOU COULD. YOUR MEN ARE HERE TO SAFEGUARD YOUR PASSAGE BACK TO YOUR SHIP.

THAT'S IT? NOTHING MORE?

IT CAN'T BE THAT SIMPLE.

THAT'S IT. GO IN, GET THE FLEECE, WALK OUT WITH IT, GET ON YOUR SHIP, AND GO HOME.

CONGRATULATIONS, JASON OF IOLCUS, YOU HAVE WHAT YOU DESERVE.

BY ZEUS'S CHILDREN!

DON'T DO THAT. HE'S ASLEEP.

MEDEA? ABSYRTUS?

WHAT'S GOING ON HERE?

I PUT HIM TO SLEEP. I'M A WITCH, REMEMBER. IT'S WHAT I DO.

BUT ... YOU? ABSYRTUS?

I TOLD YOU. HE THINKS YOU'RE THE GREATEST HERO TO EVER COME HERE.

AND ME?

WELL, I DECIDED I COULDN'T WAIT UNTIL YOU GOT BACK TO IOLCUS. THAT WOULD TAKE SUCH A LONG TIME. I'D GO MAD.

SO I'M GOING BACK WITH YOU NOW THAT YOU HAVE THE FLEECE.

BUT YOU'RE PART OF THE ROYAL FAMILY OF COLCHIS.

SO?

AND I CAN'T JUST RUN FROM HERE TO THE SHIP.

YES, YOU CAN.

NOW TAKE IT. WE HAVE TO HURRY BEFORE FATHER KNOWS WHAT'S HAPPENING.

WE CAN REACH THE BOAT BEFORE HE CAN DO ANYTHING.

WE?

ME.
YOU.
ABSYRTUS.

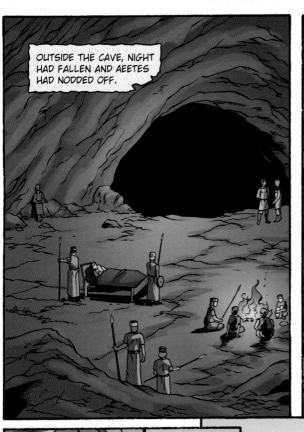

OUTSIDE THE CAVE, NIGHT HAD FALLEN AND AEETES HAD NODDED OFF.

ARGONAUTS! TO THE SHIP!

THE FLEECE! MEDEA! ABSYRTUS!

STOP THEM AT ALL COSTS!

GET THE FLEECE!

THEY'VE KIDNAPPED THE PRINCE AND PRINCESS!

THE ESCAPE TO IOLCUS

HURRY, THE WINDS ARE FAVOURABLE!

ARGONAUTS, TO THE SHIP!

ZETES, CALAIS, WE NEED YOUR FATHER'S AID!

IT IS DONE, JASON!

AFTER THEM!

BY HADES, THEY'RE USING THE SAME WIND.

AYE, AND THEIR SHIP IS FASTER. IT'S ONLY A MATTER OF TIME BEFORE THEY CATCH UP WITH US.

IF AEETES CAPTURES US, HE WILL SHOW NO MERCY!

ROW, HEROES! ROW!

HE WILL FEED US TO THE SWINE, WON'T HE?

WE WILL MAKE IT, LOVE. YOU TRUSTED ME BEFORE. YOU CAN TRUST ME AGAIN.

I WILL NOT LET HIM CAPTURE US.

PUT YOUR BACKS INTO IT!

ROW!

COME ON! COME ON!

HEE-EE-ELP ME-EE!

SAVE HIM!

ROPE! THROW HIM A ROPE!

GOT YOU, BOY. YOU'RE SAFE. YOU MUST WORSHIP POSEIDON.

AND IF YOU DON'T, NOW WOULD BE A GOOD TIME TO START.

CAREFUL!

HE'S SAFE.

I KNEW HE WOULD BE. MY FATHER WOULD NEVER LET ANYTHING HAPPEN TO HIM.

YOU WERE THAT SURE?

IT TURNED OUT THE RIGHT WAY, DIDN'T IT? DOES IT MATTER WHETHER I WAS SURE OR NOT?

AND NOW WE RETURN TO IOLCUS?

YES, THAT'S THE PLAN. I'VE GOT THE FLEECE. THE QUEST IS DONE, AND I WILL BECOME KING.

AND I WILL BE QUEEN.

OF COURSE. I PROMISED YOU I WOULD NEVER FORGET YOU.

NEVER?

NEVER.

AND I'LL ALWAYS LOVE YOU.

GLOSSARY

ABSYRTUS: prince of Colchis

AEETES: king of Colchis

AESON: father of Jason; king of Iolcus

ARGO: Jason's ship

ARGONAUTS: the heroes who sailed with Jason

ATHAMAS: a king of Iolcus

ATHENA: goddess of wisdom and war

BOREAS: the North Wind

CADMUS: founder of the Greek city of Thebes who planted the dragon teeth that grew into warriors

CALAIS: one of the twin sons of Boreas

CASTOR: one of the Greek hero twins

CHALCIOPE: Aeetes' daughter; wife of Phrixus

CHIRON: the centaur (part horse, part man) who raised Jason

EROS: god of love

HELLE: princess of Argos; daughter of Athamas and Nephele

HEPHAESTUS: the blacksmith god

HERA: wife of Zeus and goddess of the home

INO: Athamas's second wife

JASON: hero who travelled to Colchis to retrieve the Golden Fleece

MEDEA: princess of Colchis

MELAS: son of Phrixus and Chalciope

NEPHELE: cast-off queen of Iolcus

ORPHEUS: Greek hero and musician

PELEUS: famous hero; future father of Achilles

PELIAS: brother of Aeson; stole the throne of Iolcus

PHINEUS: a wise man

PHRIXUS: prince of Iolcus who was taken to Colchis by the Golden Ram

PHRONTIS: son of Phrixus and Chalciope

POLLUX: one of the Greek hero twins

POSEIDON: god of the oceans and of earthquakes

SYMPLEGADES: massive rocks in the sea that crash together when ships try to pass

ZETES: one of the twin sons of Boreas

ZEUS: chief Greek god; the god of thunder and of the sky

FURTHER READING AND WEBSITES

Evans, Cheryl and Anne Millard. *The Usborne Illustrated Guide to Myths and Legends* Usborne Publishing Ltd, 1985. Identifies the gods, goddesses, heroes and monsters of Greek mythology, recounts the most famous stories and briefly describes Greek history and culture.

Philip, Neil. *Mythology* (Eyewitness Books) Dorling Kindersley Publishing, 2005. This volume in the Eyewitness Books series uses dozens of colourful photos and illustrations to explore myths from around the world.

Mythweb. http://www.mythweb.com/index.html. This site, with a searchable encyclopedia, provides readers with information on gods, goddesses, and places in Greek myth.

Riordan, James. *Jason and the Golden Fleece* Frances Lincoln, 2005. This is a modern retelling of the adventures of Jason and the Argonauts in a picture-book format.

Thomas Bulfinch: Bulfinch's Mythology
http://www.classicreader.com/booktoc.php/sid.2/bookid.2823/
This website features one of the most popular English-language compilations of ancient myths. This classic work, which includes many Greek myths, was compiled by American Thomas Bulfinch in the 1800s.

CREATING *JASON: QUEST FOR THE GOLDEN FLEECE*

The legend of Jason and the other Greek heroes aboard the *Argo* and their quest for the Golden Fleece may have originated as a story told about the first great sailing ships built by the ancient Greeks. The legend as it is told today was first written in about 280 BC by Apollonius of Rhodes, a librarian at the great library in Alexandria, Egypt. The author also based this version on the retellings in *Bulfinch's Mythology*, *Mythology* by Edith Hamilton and *The Friendly Guide to Mythology* by Nancy Hathaway. David Mulroy of the University of Wisconsin-Milwaukee ensured historical and visual accuracy.

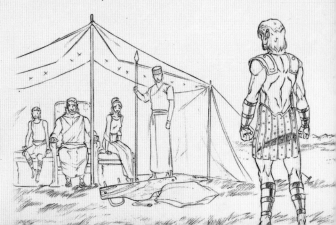

original pencil sketch from page 27

INDEX

ABOUT THE AUTHOR AND THE ARTIST

JEFF LIMKE was born and raised in North Dakota, USA, where he never braved an ocean adventure, fought skeletons or stole a golden fleece. Jeff's books for the Graphic Myths and Legends series include *King Arthur: Excalibur Unsheathed*; *Isis & Osiris: To the Ends of the Earth*; and *Thor & Loki: In the Land of Giants*. He has published other stories with Caliber Comics, Arrow Comics and Kenzer and Company.

TIM SEELEY is a professional comic book artist and writer. Hailing from the backwoods of central Wisconsin, USA, Seeley currently resides in Chicago, Illinois, where he works as staff artist for Devil's Due Publishing. His portfolio includes *G.I. Joe*, *Forgotten Realms*, and *Hack/Slash*. He thanks the ancient Greeks for having a story with zombies in it.